FORWARD

"A time is coming and has now come when the true worshipers will worship the Father in spirit and in truth, for they are the kind of worshipers the Father seeks." - John 4:23

Vineyard Music Group is dedicated to the vision of seeing our nation bow before the Lord in worship. It is our hope that these praise & worship songs bring you into the almighty presence of God in a powerful and anointed manner. Each series introduces an exciting new facet of worship allowing the listener to experience worship of the Father in spirit and in truth. VINEYARD MUSIC GROUP is a full-service worship and praise music company. We hope that this songbook is a valuable resource in facilitating worship whenever you use it.

PRAISE & WORSHIP CDs AND TAPES
Experience the music known world-wide for its power and intimacy. From dynamic live worship albums to high-quality devotional and inspirational recordings, encounter the glory of God through the beauty of music.

SONGBOOKS
Specially designed for your worship needs, the worship and praise songbooks Volumes 1 - 5 are arranged for lyrics, guitar and piano; and a Words Only Songbook is available.

Worship Product Lines Available through Vineyard Music Group:

TOUCHING THE FATHER'S HEART
Enjoy the fluid, spontaneous dynamics of a live praise and worship service. This series provides one of today's most unique approaches to involving listeners in a live worship experience.

WORSHIP SONGS OF THE VINEYARD
Each album features renown soloists, duos and group vocalists as they interpret the beauty and simplicity of Vineyard songs with a refined studio sound.

BEST LOVED WORSHIP & PRAISE SONGS FROM THE VINEYARD
Featuring praise and worship favorites, this series contains collections of songs worshipers know and love.

continued...

VINEYARD PSALMS

These collections contain only the most intimate Vineyard worship songs that allow the listener to enter into a spirit of worship during their quiet time.

CLASSICAL AND INSTRUMENTAL SERIES

Reflective and intimate songs presented through professional arrangements featuring some of Vineyard's most popular songs. The Classical Series (Volumes I and II) utilize the beauty of classical guitar while the Instrumental Series (four titles) presents calming worship songs with full orchestration.

VINEYARD WORSHIP FOR KIDS SERIES

The Worship for Kids series are contemporary recordings produced for young kids who desire to grow in worship. This series offers professional musicianship with the dynamic of children singing.

For more information, or for questions and comments regarding Vineyard music, please contact:

Vineyard Music Group
P.O. Box 68025 • Anaheim, CA 92817-0825
or call **1-800-852-VINE**
or FAX (714) 777-8119

CONTENTS

ABOVE ALL OTHERS

Words and Music by
CRAIG MUSSEAU

Solo Changes

Dm7 | Dm7/C | B♭2 | F2/A

To Chorus After Solo

(Repeat Chorus 2 Times)

6
ARMS OF LOVE
Words and Music by
CRAIG MUSSEAU
♩=76
G
D/F♯
Em7
(love.)
G
D/F♯
Em7
G
D/F♯
I sing a simp - le song of love
Em
Em/D
to my Sav -
C
(D)Em
D
ior, to my Je - sus.

G
D/F♯
I'm grate - ful for the things you've done,
Em
my lov - ing Sav -
C
Em
D
- ior,
oh pre - cious Je - sus.
Am
Em
My heart is glad
that you've
D/F♯
G
called me your own.

Am
Em
There's no place I'd rath - er be
D
G
Bm7
than in your arms of love,
C
G
Bm7
in your arms of love,
C
Hold - ing me still,
To Coda
Em
Bm7
1.
C
hold - ing me near in your arms of love.

2.
C
G
D.S. 𝄋
in your arms of love.
3.
C
D.S.S. 𝄋𝄋 al Coda
in your arms in your

Coda
C
Holding me still,
Em
Bm7
C
G
hold - ing me near in your arms of love.

ARMY OF GOD
(Joel 2:20)

Words and Music by
KEVIN PROSCH

♩=127

E

B7

E A

We are the army of God, sons of A - bra ham,

F♯m7 Bsus B E Esus E A6 2

we are a cho - sen gen - er - a - tion.

E A

Un - der a cov - e-nant, washed by his pre-cious blood,

F♯m7 Bsus B E 𝄋 A

filled with the might - y Ho - ly Ghost. And I hear the

E A E A E
sound, of the com-ing rain, as we sing the praise
F♯m7 Bsus B A E A
to the Great I Am. And the sick are healed, and the dead will
E A G♯m F♯m7
rise, and your church is the ar - my that was
Bsus To Coda 1. B 2. B E
proph-e - sied.
B7sus 3. D.S. al Coda Coda B
And I
E
A/E E 1. 2. 3. A/E E Last time A/E E Bsus B E
Your church is the ar - my. ar - my.

AWESOME BEAUTY

Words and Music by
DAPHNE RADEMAKER

D
Esus
E/G♯
A
E/A
D/A
A
are a-bove all oth - ers.
Awe - some Beau - ty,
A
E/A
D
E
A
E/A
D/A
E
To Coda
per - fect faith - ful- ness,
end - less mer - cy, might-y
D.S. al Coda
D/F♯
E/G♯
D/A
A
Lamb.
Coda
D
E
D/F♯
Lamb.
Ooh
the might- y Lamb,
E/G♯
D/A
E/B
D/A
A
the might-y Lamb.

BEFORE YOU CALL

(Isaiah 40:11, 65:24)

Words and Music by
DAPHNE RADEMAKER

G Gsus/A G/B C2
fore you call. I will an - swer you while
G Gsus/A G/B C2
you still speak. I will hear. My
Em D/F♯ G Am7 Em
ears are turned to the cry of my cho - sen ones.
D/F♯ G Gsus/A G/B C2
In my love you can rest in me.
G Gsus/A G/B Em D/F♯
For you are my ver-y own. So hold
C G/B Am7 G/B
on to the hope you have that I would draw you to my - self for

1.
Am
Am/G
Dsus
D
I will nev - er leave you a - lone.
G
C/G
Am
G
C/G
2.
F/C
C
Dsus
D
D2
I will nev - er leave you a-lone.
D
D/F♯
G
C2
I will not for - get you, I
D/F♯
G
C
G/B
ga-ther my lambs in my arms, so I will com - fort you

Am
Am7/G
Dsus
D
and car - ry you close to my heart.
D/F♯
G
C
D/F♯
G
piano solo
C
G/B
Am7
So I will com fort you,
so I will
G/B
C2
G/B
com - fort you,
so I will com- fort you
Am
Am7/G
Dsus
D
and car - ry you close to my heart.
G
C/G
1.
D/C
C
2.
C/D
G

BREAK OUR HEARTS
(Joel 2:12-14)

Words and Music by
KEVIN PROSCH

F♯m
C♯m
B
F♯m
And Fa-ther, deal with our car-nal de-sires, to move in your pow-
C♯m
B
F♯m
C♯m
B
er but not live the life, and to love our neigh - bor with all that we have,
F♯m
C♯m
B
Bsus
B
and keep our tongues from say-ing things we have not seen.
1.
E
A
F♯m
E
A
Oh, break our hearts with the things that break yours. If we sow in tears,
F♯m
E
A
F♯m
we will reap in joy, that we might pass through your re-fin - ing fire,

E
A
F♯m
E
A
where bro-ken-ness a-waits on the oth-er side. (Bro-ken-ness a-waits
F♯m
E
A
F♯m
on the oth-er side.)
2. Bsus
B
E
A
bro - ken - ness.
But there will be a day
F♯m
E
A
F♯m
when the na-tions will bow and our Lord will be King o-ver all the earth.
E
A
F♯m
And he will be the on - ly one,

Additional Lyrics

Verse 2: Raise up an army like Joel saw,
your church that is stronger than ever before.
They do not break ranks when they plunge through defenses,
but the fear of the Lord will be their wisdom.
That they might weep as Jesus wept,
a fountain of tears for the wounded and lost.
Who ever heard of an army of God
that conquered the earth by
weeping and mourning and brokenness?

22

CELEBRATE THE LORD

♩= 144

Words and Music by
TERRY BUTLER

G Em7 F C G
jah, cel - e - brate the Lord, sing Him a new song,
To Coda
Em7 F C G Gmaj7
cel - e - brate the Lord, let's cel - e - brate.
Dm/G C/G
1.
2. D.S. al Coda
C D♯°7
For our
Coda
G Gmaj7 Dm/G C/G G
Gmaj7 Dm/G C/G C G

CHILDREN OF LIGHT

(Psalm 95:6,7)

♩=142

Words and Music by
ANDY PARK

A D/A Esus E F♯m7 D Esus E

(F♯m7)
A D Esus E

We are the chil-dren of light,
We are the chil-dren of God,

(F♯m7)
A D Esus E

we are chil-dren of day, so let us
made in the im-age of Christ, and on the

D A E A

wor - ship him in whom we have our be - ing un-til the
day he comes we shall be made like him for we shall

Repeat 1st time only.

F♯m7 D Esus E

com - ing of the Lord.
see him as he is.

3. We are the soldiers of Christ
Dressed for the battle on high
So let us call on him for he will fight the battle
And we will march with him on that day

4. We are the faithful of God
We will endure 'til the end
So let us run the race that he has set before us
To win the crown of righteousness

COME AND FILL ME UP

Words and Music by
BRIAN DOERKSEN

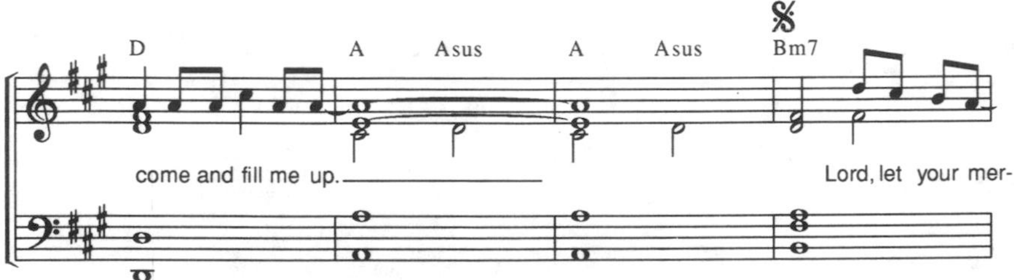

E A F♯m Bm7
cy - wash - a - way all of my sin. Fill me com-plete-
E A F♯m E D
ly - with - your - love once a-gain. I need you,
A D Esus E D
I want you, I love your pre - sence. I need you,
1st Time - D.C.
2nd Time - D.S.
3rd Time - D.S.S.
A/C♯ D Esus E
I want you, I love - your pres - ence.
Last Time
A Asus A Asus A Asus A Asus A

DANIEL 9

Words and Music by
ANDY PARK

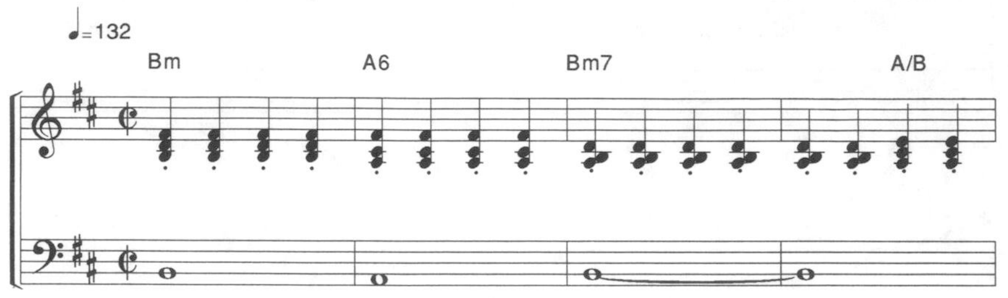

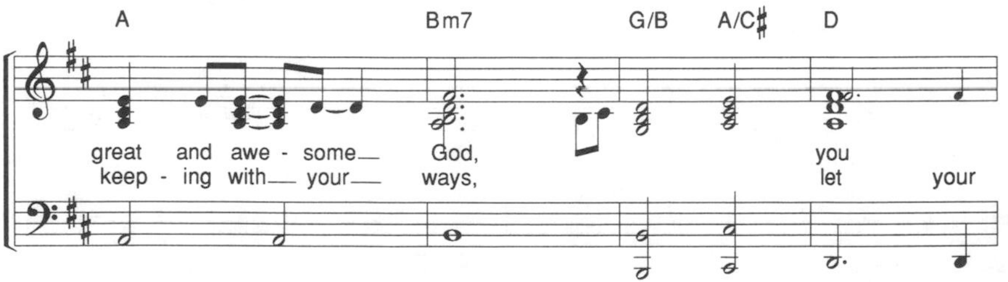

A Bm7 A
keep your cov - e - nant of love with all who
an - ger now be turned a - way. For we are your
G A A/C♯ Bm7 A
love you and all who fol - low your com -
peop - le, we are the church that bears your
1.
D A/C♯ D
mands. Oh Lord, the
A Bm7 A G
great and awe - some God. Keep with
G/B A/C♯ D
us your cov - e - nant of love. We are your

G
A
Bm7
G
peop - le and the church that bears your name.
Bm7
Asus
G(add9)
Oh Lord for-give us.
G
Bm7
Asus
3rd Time - To Coda
G(add9)
Oh Lord for-give us.
2.
Bm7
Bm7
A
Bm7
A
name.
Bm7
A
Bm7
A
We have sinned and done wrong, we have

G
A
Bm7
A
turned a - way from your laws.
Bm7
A
Bm7
We have turned from your com - mands.
Ex-tend, oh
D.S.
G
A
Bm7
A/C♯
Lord, your mer - ci-ful hand.
Coda
G
Bm7
Asus
Oh Lord for-give us.
G(add9)
G
Bm7
Oh Lord for-give us.

DESIRE ONLY YOU

Words and Music by
RANDY & TERRY BUTLER

A B E A B C♯m Amaj7 B/A
hearts, they turn a - way. Re - store us to the place where we de - si - re on - ly You,
To Coda
A2 F♯m9 B/F♯ F♯m7 B/E E
de - si - re on - ly You. Fill our hearts, oh Lord, with Your
B/C♯ C♯m Amaj7 B/A F♯m7 A/B E
right - eous - ness. Re - new in us the joy of sal - va - tion.
D.S. al Coda
Ov - er -
CODA
F♯m7 Amaj7 B/A A2
De - si - re on - ly You, de -
F♯m9 B/F♯ F♯m7 Amaj7 B/A A2 A2/B E
si - re on - ly You, de - si - re on - ly You.

DRAW NEAR TO ME

Words and Music by
JOHN BARNETT

1. 3.
2. 4.
D
G/A
A
G/A
A
G/A
Lord, my Fa - ther.
face, my Fa - ther.
Fill my
D
Bm7
G(add9)
Em9
D
A
Draw near to me,
draw near to me,
To Coda
1.
D
Bm7
Em9
Em7
Asus
A
draw near to me
my Fa - ther,
my
G
D
Fa - ther.
Lord this
2.
D.S. al Coda
A
Asus A
Coda
A
G
D
my Fa - ther.

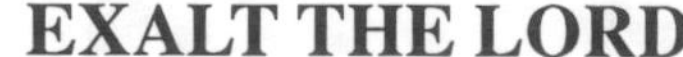

EXALT THE LORD

Words and Music by
DANNY DANIELS

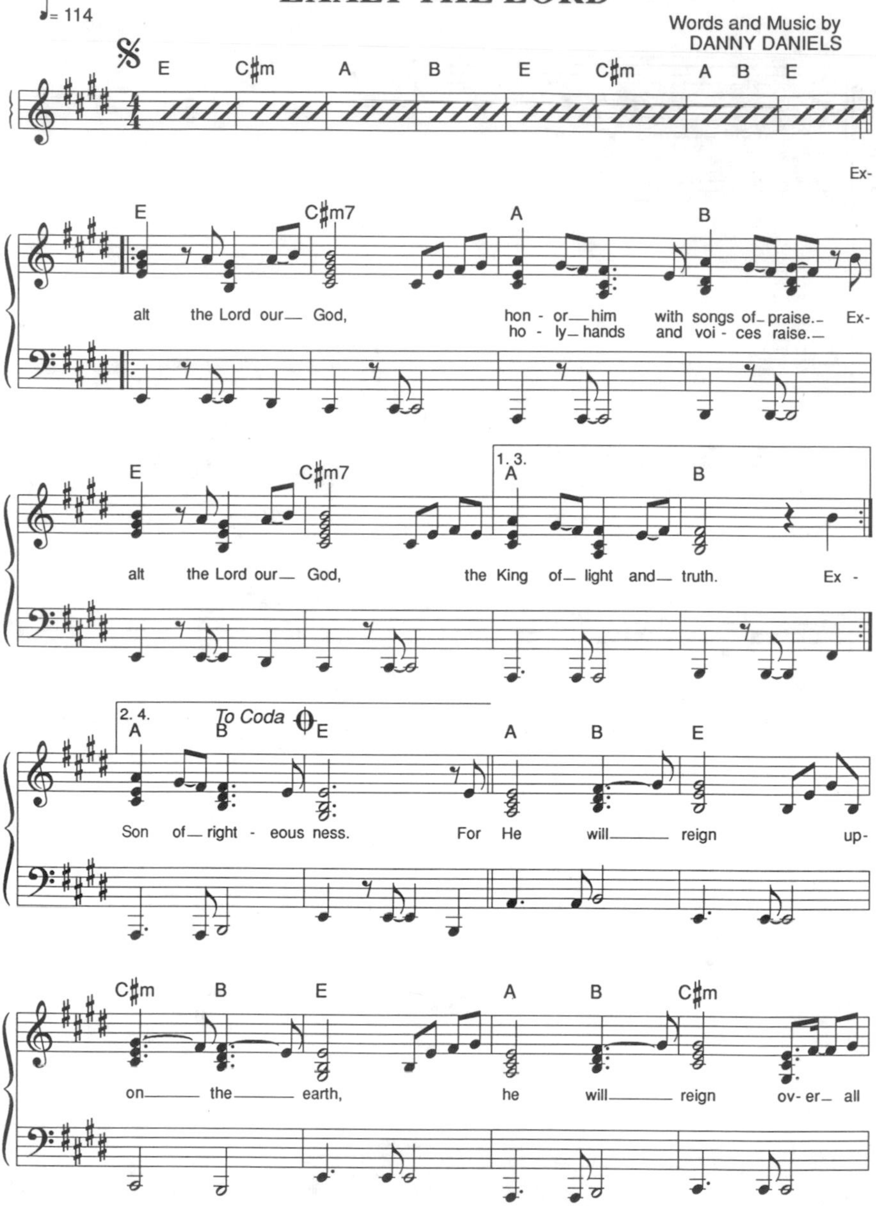
♩= 114
E C♯m A B E C♯m A B E
Ex-
E C♯m7 A B
alt the Lord our God, hon - or him with songs of praise. Ex-
ho - ly hands and voi - ces raise.
E C♯m7 A B
1. 3.
alt the Lord our God, the King of light and truth. Ex -
2. 4.
To Coda
A B E A B E
Son of right - eous ness. For He will reign up-
C♯m B E A B C♯m
on the earth, he will reign ov - er all

F♯m7 B A B E

na - tions. For he is King a-

C♯m B E A B C♯m

bove all kings, he is king now and for-

D.S. 𝄋 al Coda

D B

ev - er. Ex -

Coda

E C♯m A B E B/D♯ C♯m A

ness. the Son of right-eous ness. -

B E B/D♯ C♯m B A B E

EXALT THE LORD

(Psalm 99:5, 9)

Words and Music by
CINDY RETHMEIER

♩= 68

Em7 D Em7 D

Em7 D Em7 D Em7

Women: Ex - alt the Lord our God

Men: Ex - alt the Lord our God and wor -

D Em7 D Em7

and wor - ship at his (feet.)

- ship at his feet. Ex - alt

Em7 D Em7 D
and wor - ship at his feet. For he is ho -
feet. For he is ho -
G Em7 Cmaj7
-ly For the Lord our God, he is ho -
(you are)
D G Em7 Cmaj7 D
-ly. For the Lord our God, he is ho - ly. For the Lord
(you are)
G Em7 Cmaj7 D
our God, he is ho - ly. Yes the Lord
(you are)
G Em7 To Coda 1 Cmaj7 D
our God, he is ho - ly.
(you are)
Em7 D Em7 D D.S. al Coda
2. Cmaj7 D D.S. al Coda
ho - ly. For the Lord
Coda
Cmaj7 D G
ho - ly.

FIRE OF GOD

Words and Music by
CRAIG MUSSEAU

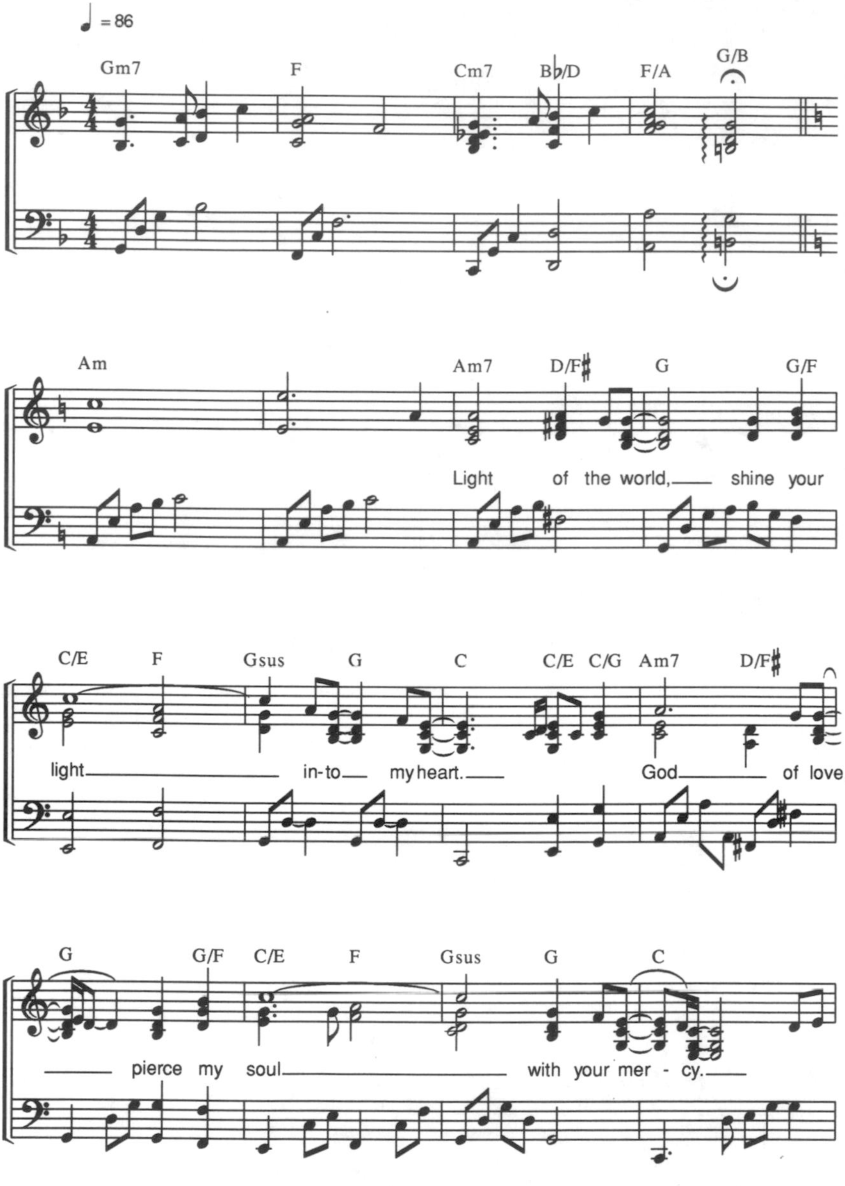

♩ = 86

Gm7 F Cm7 B♭/D F/A G/B

Am Am7 D/F♯ G G/F

Light of the world, shine your

Gm7 F G/B
So we might know your glo - ry, so we might see your face.
C C/E F Gm7 F G
So we can feel your heart beat and hear you call our nam
C Am7 D/F♯ G G/F C/E F
Fine
Fire of God, burn a - way
Gsus G C C/E C/G Am7 D/F♯ G G/F
what is not ho - ly. Je - sus, take our
C/E F Gsus G C
hearts and make them new.

GETHSEMANE
(Matthew 26:36-46)

Words and Music by
CRAIG MUSSEAU

♩= 145

Am Am/G G

Am Gsus G

1. My soul is ov - er - whelmed
2. *see bottom of last page*

Dm7 C/E Gsus G

to the point of death.

Am G

Sor - row ov - er - takes me,

Dm7 C/E G

dark - ness looms all a - round.

Dm7
C/E
Gsus
G
There's no light to be found.
C
G
It's a long hard road that you've
Am
G
F
Dm7
Gsus
put me on and I am all a - lone.
C
C/E
G
But I choose to die for the
3rd time - To Coda
4th time - To Coda
Am
G
F
Dm7
Gsus
ones that you have giv - en me.
G
F
G/F
F
Not my will, but

G
1.
C
yours be done.
C/E
F
G/F
F
Not my will, but
To Coda
G
C
G/B
yours be done.
2.
C
done.
F
G/F
F
G
Not my will, but yours be
Am
F
G/F
F
G/B
F/A
G
F/A
G/B
D.S. al Coda
done.

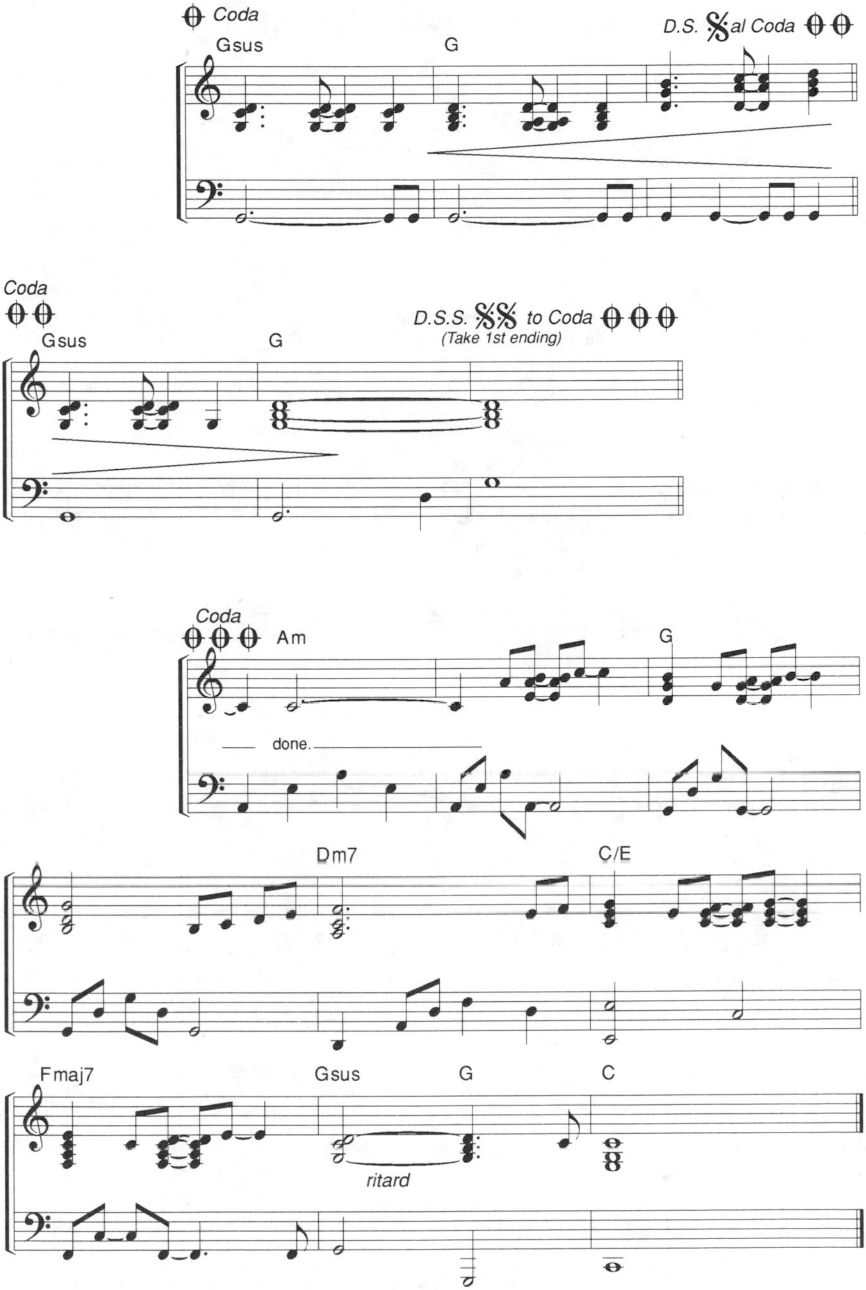

Coda

Am G

done.

Dm7 C/E

Fmaj7 Gsus G C

ritard

2. Father, if it is not possible for this cup to be taken from me,
   Then I will drink it, for my life is in your hands and you must fulfill your plan.

GLORY AND PRAISE

Words and Music by
ANDY PARK

E
E/D
D2
Wor - thy is the Lamb who was
Now to him who sits on the throne and to the
A2
E
slain, who was slain.
Lamb, who was slain.
E
E/D
D2
Wor - thy is the Lamb, who was
Now be praise and hon-or and glo - ry and pow-er for
A2
Bsus
B
slain, who was slain,
ev - er, and pow-er for - ev - er.
E
D2
1. to re-cieve pow-er and wealth,
2. Wor - thy of pow-er and wealth,
3. (Spontaneous singing)
4. to the Lamb be pow-er and wealth. Un -

A2
E
Esus
to re - ceive wis- dom and strength.
wor - thy of wis- dom and strength,
to the Lamb be wis- dom and strength, un -

E
E/D
D
To re - ceive hon - or and glo - ry.
wor - thy of hon - or and glo - ry,
to the Lamb be hon - or and glo - ry. Un -

A2
1.
E
to re - ceive glo- ry and praise.
wor - thy of glo- ry and
to the Lamb be glo- ry and

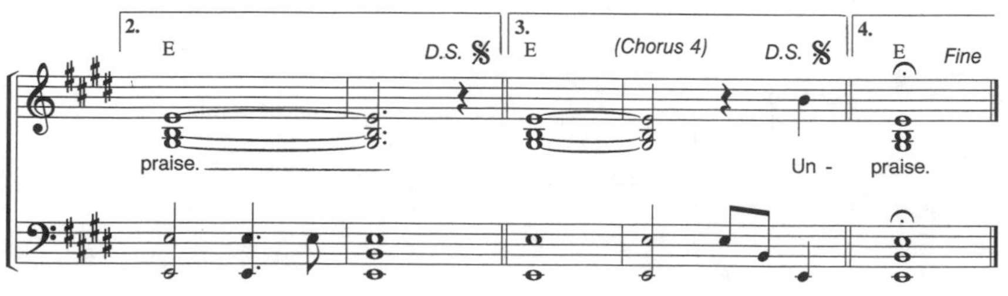
2.
E
D.S.
3.
E
(Chorus 4)
D.S.
4.
E
Fine
praise.
Un -
praise.

In a loud voice they sang,

"Worthy is the Lamb,

who was slain,

to receive power and wealth

and wisdom and strength

and honor and glory

and praise!"

- Revelation 5:12

50

GOOD TO ME
Words and Music by
CRAIG MUSSEAU
♩ = 60
G C Em7 Am7 D
G C Em Em/D D/C C
I cry out for your hand of mer - cy to heal me.
G C Em D D/C C
I am weak, I need your love to free me. Oh
G/B C G/B C
Lord, my rock, my strength in weak - ness, come
Em Bm7 C2
1.
2.
res - cue me, oh Lord. You are my

D
G/B
C
Dsus
D/F♯
G
hope, your pro - mise ne - ver fails me. And my de -
D
G/B
C
Dsus
D/F♯
G
sire is to fol - low you for - e - ver. For you are
C
G/B
Am7
G
D/F♯
D
good, for you are good, for you are good to me. For you are
To Coda
D.S. al Coda
(Take 2nd ending)
C
G/B
Am7
G
D/F♯
good, for you are good, for you are good to me.
CODA
(Repeat ad lib)
D/F♯
D
C
G/B
Am7
D/F♯
D
me. For you are good, for you are good, for you are good to me. For you are

HEAVEN SINGS

Words and Music by
CRAIG MUSSEAU

2. He came down to lead us to the Father, make him known to all mankind.
He showed his heart was full of mercy, healed the sick, gave sight to the blind.
He came to be a servant, to give his life away to set us free,
And now he reigns in glory ruling in love and purity.

HELP ME TO LOVE

Words and Music by
DANNY DANIELS

Emaj7
G♯m
C♯m
B
where and when and how you
A
F♯m
move. Please draw me near,
B
G♯m7
Amaj7
help me to hear. Come and fill me
G♯m
with you,
Amaj7
G♯m
C♯
Ho ly Spir - it. Come and

Amaj7
G♯m
fill me with you,
Amaj7
Ho ly
G♯m
C♯
F♯m
Spir it.
Help me to love
B
E
To Coda
1.
the things you love.
Amaj7
F♯m11
D.S.
Come and

Coda
C♯m7
F♯m
B
Help me to love the things you
E
A
F♯m11
Emaj9
love.

HELP US OUR GOD

(Psalm 79:9)

Words & Music by
BRIAN DOERKSEN & CINDY RETHMEIER

D/A A/C♯ D A Esus E F♯m
and for-give all our sins. Help us our
D E F♯m
God, we come to you des-p'rate-ly need-y. Help us our
D E F♯m E/G♯ A
God, may your mer-cy come quick-ly to meet us. Help us our
D A D F♯m E A/C♯
Help us our God, help us our God,
God, help us our God. Help us our
D A/C♯ D/E E D/F♯ A/C♯
ritard
God for your name's sake. Help
E/G♯ D/A 1. A
us our God.
2. F♯m7 D 2 2 E D.S. 3. A
ad lib

60
HERE AM I
(Acts 4:23-31)
Words and Music by
BRIAN DOERKSEN
♩=95
8vb
D G6 2 D2/F♯ G6 2 D
D D2/F♯
Here am I.
Send me Lord.
G A G D
In my weak-ness I know you will be strong
D2/F♯
Here am I.
Em-pow'r me.
repeat this section 2nd time only
G A G
Stretch out your hand to heal the sick,
A G D G
on repeat-
jump to chorus
stretch out your arm and set the pris'-ners free.

D
Come fill me,
D2/F♯
G
A
G
with mer - cy.
Send me out to heal the bro - ken-heart-
D
- ed.
Come fill me,
D2/F♯
G
A
with bold - ness.
I will speak your
G
A
G
D
words of life.
I will go in your au - thor - i - ty.
(chorus)
A/C♯
G/B
A
D
(G add9)
Oh
oh.
1. 2.
A/C♯
G/B
A
D
2nd Time -D.S.
3. A
G(add9)

HIS BANNER OVER ME

(Song of Songs 2:4)

Words and Music by
KEVIN PROSCH

G
love.
G
I am my be-lov-ed's and
I am my be-lov - ed's and he is mine.
he is mine.
Yes, I am my be-lov-ed's and he is mine.
I am my be-lov-ed's and he is mine.
C
And his ban-ner o-ver
G
me is love.

C
Yes, his ban-ner ___ o-ver
after solos only
me, o-ver me, ___ is ___
G Am7 G/B C2
love. ___
G Am7 G/B C2
And we can
G Am7 G/B
feel the love of God ___ in this place, we be - lieve your good - ness, we re -

C2
G
Am7
ceive your grace. We de - light our - selves_ at your ta - ble, oh God,_ you do
G/B
C2
1.
all things well,_ just look at our lives._ He
2.
C2
C G/B Am7
G
Am7
Repeat as needed for instrumental solos.
G/B
C
G
Am7
G/B
C
D.S.
Last time only
C2
C G/B Am7
G
And yeshis

66
I BOW DOWN
Words and Music by
CINDY RETHMEIER
♩=74
A D/A A D/A
A E F♯m D Bm7 Esus E
1. I bow down be - fore you Lord.
2. I kneel down be - fore you Lord.
3. instrumental verse
A E F♯m D Bm7 Esus E
I bow down be - fore you Lord.
I kneel down be - fore you Lord.
D A F♯m
Ho ly and faith - ful, right-eous and
Re - deem er and Heal - er, Al - might - y
D Bm7 E Esus E D E
true, you are my King. You are
God, you are my King.

A D A D
Je - sus. You're my Sav - ior and with
A E/A D Bm7
all that is with - in me I bow down be-fore
kneel
1. E
you.
2.4. E D E D.S.
you. You are
3. E
you.
5. E Esus E
you.
ritard
D A F♯m
Ho - ly and faith - ful, right-eous and
D Bm7 E Esus E A
true. You are my King.

I HOPE IN YOU

Words and Music by
CRAIG MUSSEAU

𝄋

D E A D/A E

me, oh Lord. I will hope in you. I

A D E A D/A E

look to your un-fail - ing love. I will hope in you, for you are mer-

D E D/F♯ E/G♯

ci-ful to me, and you are gra - cious to me, and your love

D.S. 𝄋 al Coda
(Take 1st Ending)

A D F♯m E 1. To Coda 𝄌 2. F♯m7 E/G♯

will nev-er fail. I hope in you. I hope In you. I will

𝄌 Coda

E F♯m7 E/G♯ A Bm7 A/C♯ E A

'Cause your love will nev - er fail.

I NEED YOU TO HOLD ME

Words & Music by
BRENDA LEFAVE

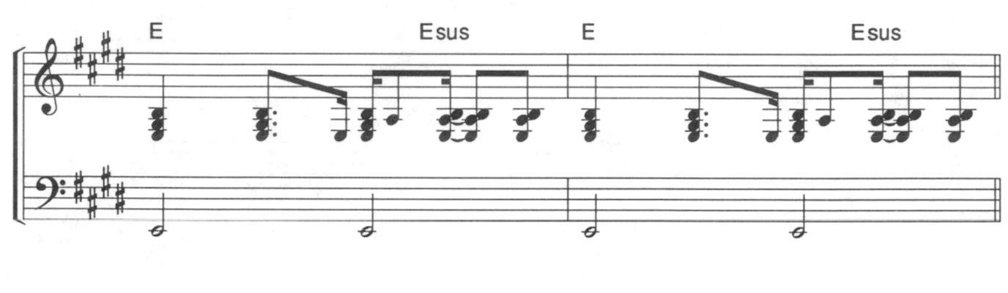

E A E
need you to show me how
E/G♯ A Bsus B
rest - ing in your arms can be so good. Oh,
(2nd time: F♯m7 A B B/D♯ E E/G♯ A E/G♯
A B E A
hold me hold me Fa - ther, nev - er let me go.
F♯m7 A B B/D♯)
B E
Hold me tight, hold me clos - er still. 'Cause
A B C♯m
you've been on - ly kind to me and in your arms is where

1.
A
Bsus
B
I need to be.
2.
A
B
D.S.
I need to be.
Oh,
3.
A
E
F♯m
E/G♯
in your arms
is
A
E
F♯m
E/G♯
where
in your arms
is
A
Bsus
B
where
I need to be.

2. I need you to walk with me
Hand in hand we'll run and play
And I need you to talk to me
Tell me again you'll stay

I WANT TO BE FAITHFUL

Words & Music by
CRAIG MUSSEAU

G D G
ser - vant. I want to be faith - ful to you,
Je - sus.
A Em Bm7
I want to be true Lord. What-ev - er you say,
G A 1.D
I will do, I will o - bey.
D/F♯ 2.D
I want to be faith -
3. 4. Em7 D
Help me to I want to be faith -
5.D G D/F♯ Em7 D2

I WANT TO KNOW YOU

Words and Music by
BRIAN DOERKSEN & CINDY RETHMEIER

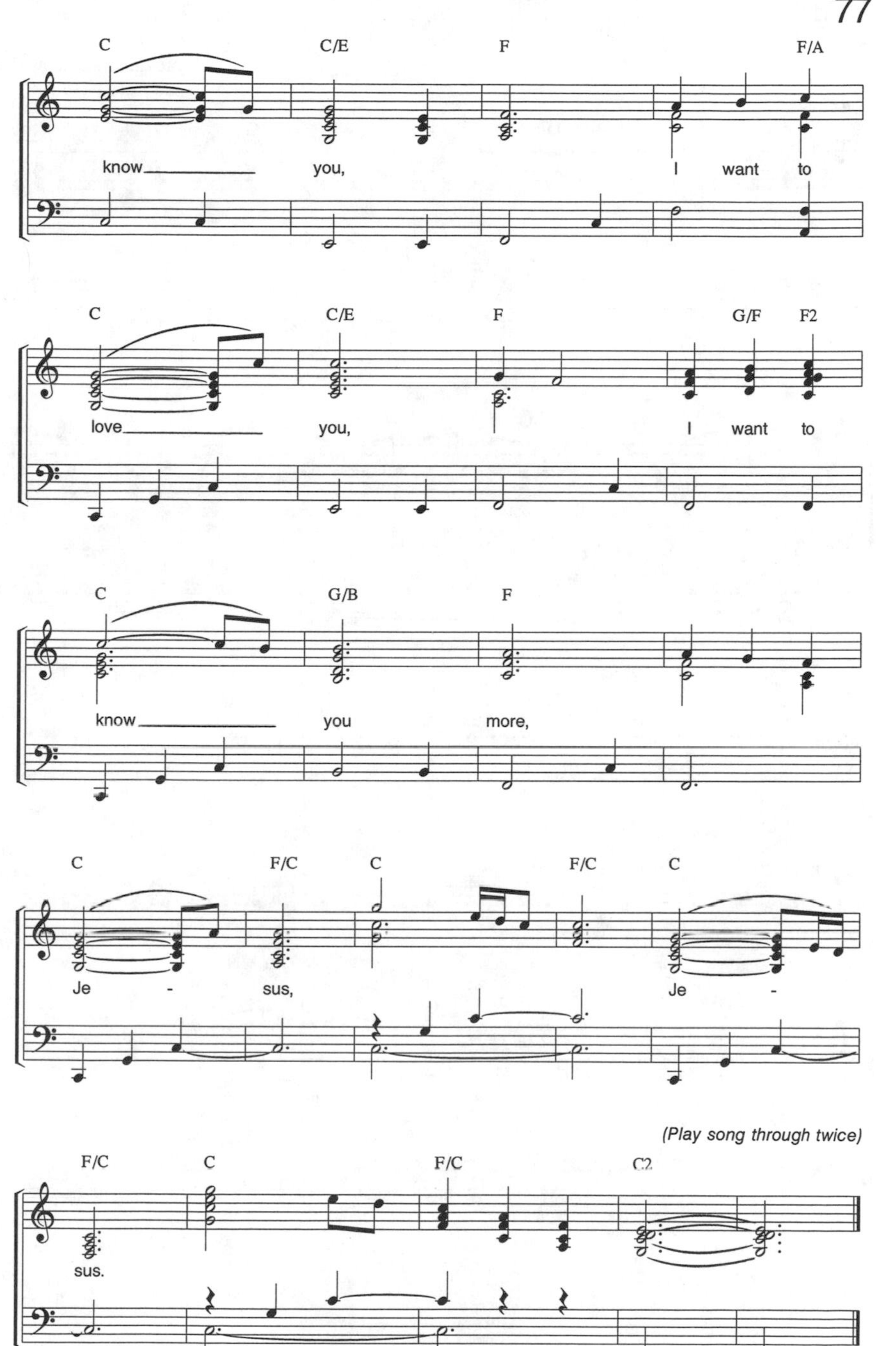
C
C/E
F
F/A
know
you,
I
want
to
C
C/E
F
G/F
F2
love
you,
I
want
to
C
G/B
F
know
you
more,
C
F/C
C
F/C
C
Je
-
sus,
Je
-
(Play song through twice)
F/C
C
F/C
C2
sus.

IMMANUEL

Words and Music by
ANDY PARK

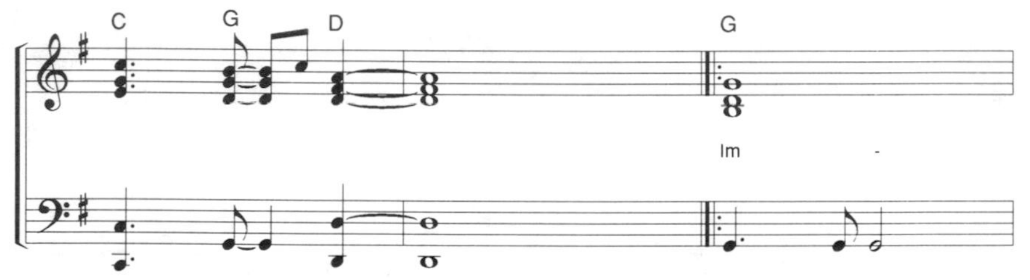

D G C G D
Im - man - u - el is God with us.
Em D G
He is born for us,
C G D Em
Christ the long a wait - ed Mes - si - ah,
C D G C G D
Im - man - u - el has come to dwell

G G C G D
with us!
fine
Em D C
Now a light has dawned
Born in a man - ger, a
Am7 G D
in the land of dark - ness.
bab - y poor and low - ly.
Em D C
Now the cho - sen One has
Born of a vir - gin in

Am7 G D

come to us.
Christ the Lord.

Bm7 Em C

We have seen his light, we have seen his
Glo - ry to the Lord, all glo - ry in the

G D Bm7

glo - ry, shin - ing
high - est. Peace on

Em C G D

in the dark like the ris - ing sun.
earth to men who will fol - low him.

ISAIAH VI

Words and Music by
ANDY PARK

D C G/B Am
ho - ly, ho - ly is the
glo - ry, glo - ry to the
F D/F# D C G
Lord God Al-might - y. 1. All the an - gels
2. All your peo - ple
Lord God Al-might - y. 3. The whole earth is
Fmaj7 Em7 G/D D C G Em7
cry out ho - ly. All the an - gels ex -
cry out ho - ly. All your peo - ple ex -
filled with glo - ry. The whole earth will ex -
Am7 G/B Dsus D C G
alt your name cry - ing ho - ly,
alt your name
alt your name
Fmaj7 Em7 G/D D Em C
ho - ly, ho - ly, ho - ly

To Coda
1. 2.
Dsus D
G
D/G
C/G
is the Lord.
3.
D.S. al Coda
Dsus D
Em7
Am7
G/B
C/D
Lord.
All the

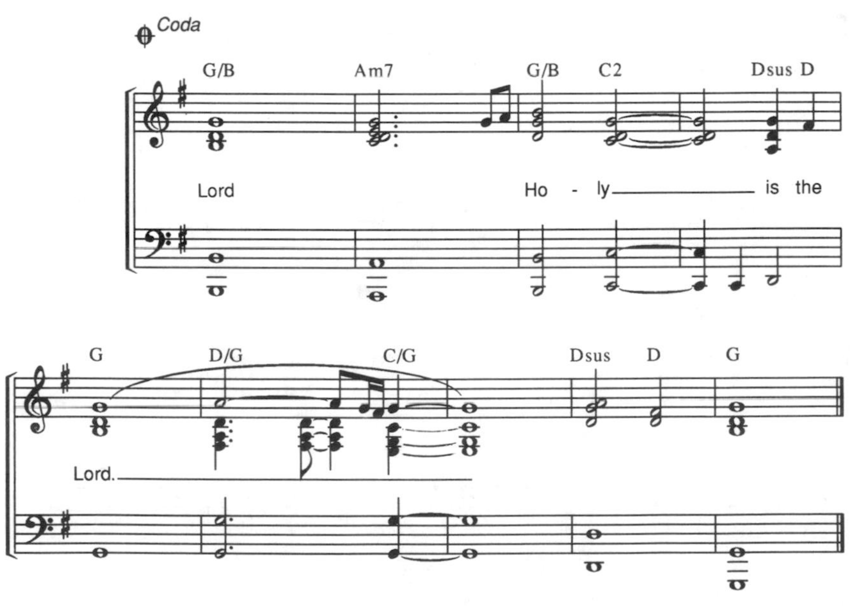
Coda
G/B
Am7
G/B
C2
Dsus D
Lord
Ho - ly
is the
G
D/G
C/G
Dsus D
G
Lord.

In the year that King Uzziah died,

I saw the Lord seated on a throne,

high and exalted,

and the train of his robe filled the temple.

Above him were seraphs,

each with six wings:

With two wings they covered their faces,

with two they covered their feet,

and with two they were flying.

And they were calling to one another:

"Holy, holy, holy is the Lord Almighty;

the whole earth is full of his glory."

At the sound of their voices

the doorposts and thresholds shook

and the temple was filled with smoke.

- Isaiah 6:1-4

86
JESUS REIGNS
Words and Music by
CRAIG MUSSEAU
♩ = 156
E Esus E Esus E/B
A E/B Cdim7 C♯m7 E/B B
E E Esus E
Je - sus is exalt - ed,
Esus B A
Je - sus is praised.
G♯m A E/B Cdim7 C♯m7
He de - serves all the glo - ry we

E/B
B
E
ren-der un-to his ho-ly name. Je-sus
C♯m
B
A
F♯m7
B
E
reigns, to-geth-er we'll sing of his glo-
B/D♯
C♯m
G♯m
ry. Je-sus reigns, we'll
Amaj7
A/B
E
C♯m
B
A
sing of his won-drous love. Je-sus reigns,
F♯m7
B
E
B/D♯
his Spi-rit is mov-ing up-on us. Je-sus

C♯m G♯m
1.
Amaj7 A/B E
reigns, his po wer is here from a bove.
2.
Amaj7 A/B E
F Fsus
power is here from a bove. Je - sus is exalt-
F Fsus C
ed, Je - sus is praised.
B♭ Am B♭ F/C C♯dim7 Dm7
He de- serves all the glo - ry we
F/C C F
ren - der un - to his ho - ly name. Je- sus

Dm C B♭ Gm7 C F C/E
reigns, to-geth-er we'll sing of his glo - ry. Je-sus
Dm Am B♭maj7 B♭/C F
reigns, we'll sing of his won-drous love. Je-sus
Dm C B♭ Gm7 C F C/E
reigns, his Spi - rit is mov - ing up- on us. Je-sus
To Coda
D.S. al Coda
Dm Am B♭maj7 B♭/C F
reigns, his po-wer is here from a- bove. Je-sus
Coda
F B♭maj7 B♭/C F

LET US DRAW NEAR

Words and Music by
CRAIG MUSSEAU

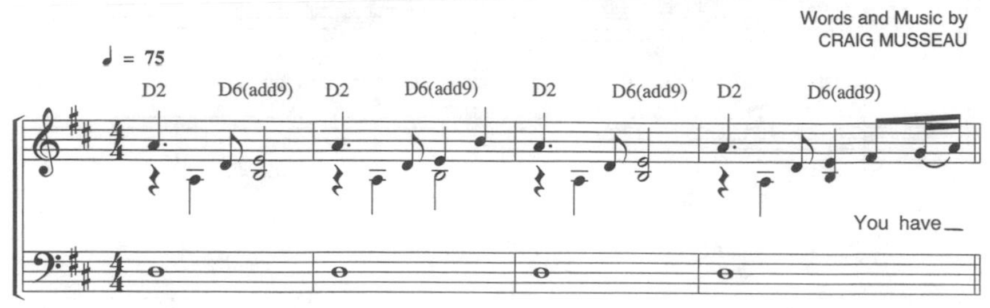

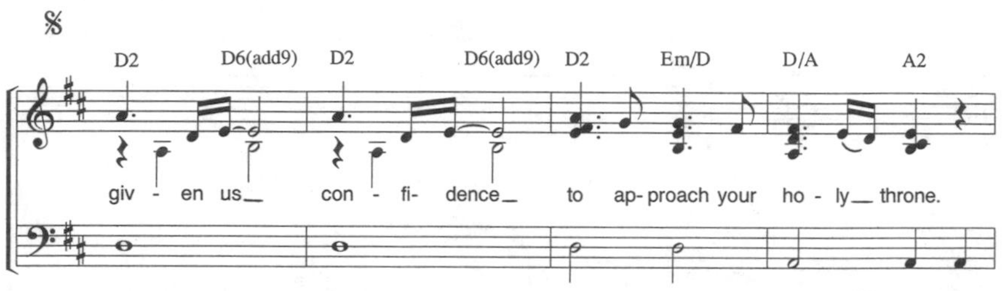

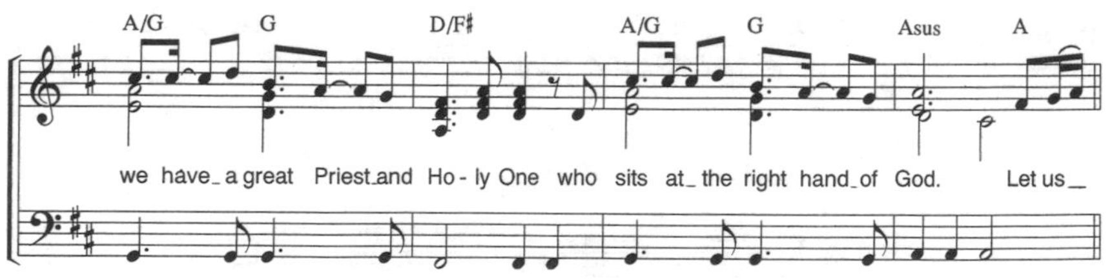

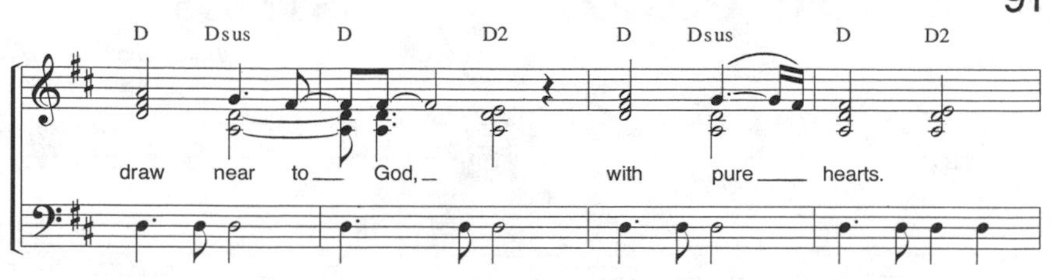
D Dsus D D2 D Dsus D D2
draw near to God, with pure hearts.

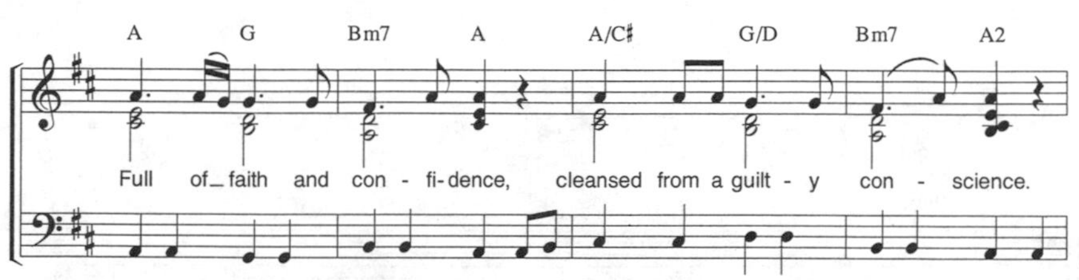
A G Bm7 A A/C♯ G/D Bm7 A2
Full of faith and con - fi- dence, cleansed from a guilt - y con - science.

G Gmaj7 G Gmaj7 Em7 Bm7 A/C♯
Washed in pure wat - er we hope in you, for you are

To Coda
D.S. al Coda
G/D D2 D6(add9) D2 D6(add9)
faith- ful, yes you are faith- ful. You have

Coda
(Repeat as often as desired)
D G/D
faith- ful. Fine For you are faith- ful, yes you are

LORD COME THIS CHRISTMAS

Words and Music by
ANDY PARK

♩=85

C

A - way in a man - ger ___ as a child he lay,

Dm7/C

Dm7 Dm7/G G Dm/C C

shep - herds came to wor - ship and a - dore ___ him.

Dm/C C C

Deep in the mea - dow the ___ an - gels sang,

Dm7/C Dm7 3

glo - ry to God in the

Dm7/G
G
Dm/C
C
F/A
G/B
high - est and peace to men.
C
C/E
G/F
F
D/F♯
He came at Christ - mas to bring his
G
G/F
C/E
Cmaj7
G/F
F
light, to a poor and low - ly man - ger, he
C
Gsus
G
C/E
F
came that night.
Gsus
G/B
C/E
F
Gsus
G/B
As you

C
Dm7/C
came to the man - ger you have come to
Dm7
Dm7/G
G
me, you have shown the bright - ness of your
Dm/C
C
Dm/C
C
C
glo - ry. Now as I
Dm7/C
wor - ship, I have just one plea,
Dm7
Dm7/G
G
Dm/C
C
as you came that Christ - mas, Lord please come to me.
F/A
G/B
C
C/E
G/F
F
Lord come this Christ - mas,

D/F♯
G
G/F
C/E
come bring your light. Won't you come this
G/F
F
C
Gsus
G
D.S. 𝄋
Christ - mas to my home, to my heart.
C/E
F
Gsus
G/B
C
C/E
Lord come this
G/F
F
C
Gsus
G
Christ - mas to my home and to my
C
heart.

LORD OF THE POOR

Words and Music by
BRIAN DOERKSEN

G D G A
who know their need. Pour out your Fa -
Bm E Asus
ther's love on the fa - ther - less chil -
A D A
dren. Lord of the poor,
Bm A D
God of the weak and help - less ones, stretch out your arm
A Bm Asus A
and be a safe re - fuge for the ones

G
D
A
To Coda
who have no hope at all.
Em
D
A - rise oh Lord
G
D
Em
D/F♯
and have com - pas - sion on the poor and
G
Bm
A
need - y ones.
1.
G
A
2.
G
D.S. al Coda

Coda
A G D
who have no hope at all.
A Em D/F♯
A-rise oh Lord
G D/F♯ Em D/F♯
and have com-pas - sion on the poor and
G Bm A G
need - y ones.
D G D D/F♯ G D
You have cho-sen the poor to be rich in faith.

100

LORD YOU ARE MY SHEPHERD

Words and Music by
ANDY PARK

E
G♯7
C♯m11
A2
3
B
right-eous-ness, and you lead __ me through dark-ness and pain.

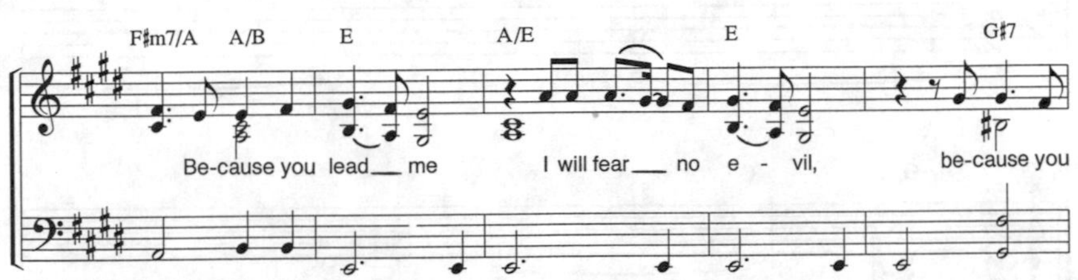
F♯m7/A
A/B
E
A/E
E
G♯7
Be-cause you lead __ me I will fear __ no e - vil, be-cause you

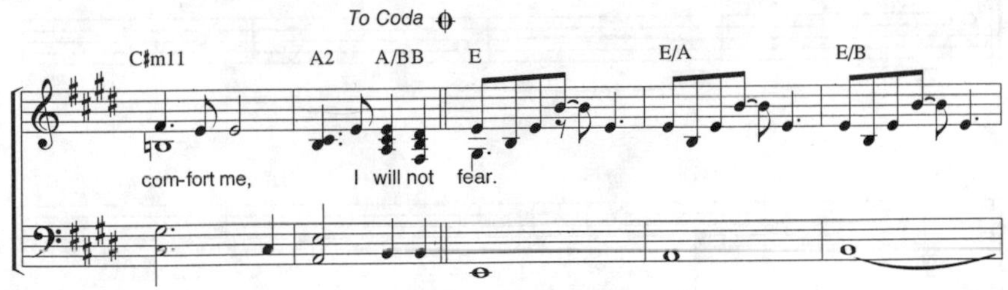
To Coda
C♯m11
A2
A/BB
E
E/A
E/B
com-fort me, I will not fear.

D.S. al Coda
CODA
E/G♯
A2
E/B
C♯m11
fear. Be-cause you com-fort me,

A2
A/B B
E
E/A
E/B
E
I will not fear.
ritard.

MAY I BE KNOWN

Words and Music by
CINDY RETHMEIER

G F C F
you. Let me know you. Je -
C/E G Gsus G Am7
sus, you are my Lord. I want to know
G F G F
you. Lord, I must know you. Je -
G 1.3. C G/C C6 G/C C G/C C6
sus, you are my God.
G/C C 2. C G/C C6 F G
D.S. al Fine
May I be God. that I may
Fine

104 MY FATHER'S WILL

(John 5:19,30)

Words and Music by
ANDY PARK

2. I can hear my Father speaking to me
I know that he is with me
For he has made his home in me
And he will never leave me

3. I will speak the words my Father teaches me
Apart from him I cannot see
Alone I can do nothing
I only want to please him

106 MY HEART THIRSTS FOR THE LORD

2. I stretch my hands out to you, *(I stretch my hands out to you)*
My soul cries out to you, *(My soul cries out to you)*

NOW AND FOREVER

Words and Music by
EDDIE ESPINOSA

Dm7 G Em7 Am Dm7
we be-hold your face in all your splen-dor we will lift our voice and
I I will lift my voice and
Fmaj7 Gsus4 G Dm9
sing our praise to you. Lord, we will wor-ship you
sing my praise to you. Lord, I will wor-ship you
G Em7 Am Dm
now and for - ev - er; Now and for - ev - er, we'll
I'll
1. G C C7 2. Gsus4 G
sing your praise. Lord, we will sing your
sing your praise. Lord, I will
1st time D.S.
C F/C C F/C C
praise.

O COME AND SEE

Words and Music by
CARLA WHITE & BELINDA LAMS

C♯
C♯/F
F♯m7
One day he'll die for the sins of — the world,
C♯
C♯/F
F♯m7
Bm7/E
one day he'll die for — me. —
A
D
A
O come - and see the Lord — as — he sleeps,
Bm7
F♯m7
come now be - hold our new - born — King, —
Bm7
Bm7/E
A
D2
God's pre - cious Son, our new - born — King.
A
D2
A
ritard

112

O HOLY LORD

Am G D Dsus2 D C2 G
To Coda
cry to you, make us me ho - ly like you, make us me
1.
C2 G
ho - ly like you.
2.
D.S. al Coda
C2 D
ho - ly like you. O
CODA
C2 G Am G
ho - ly like you. I love you
D Dsus2 D Am G D Dsus2 D Am G
Lord. I need you Lord. I want you
D C2 G C2 G
Lord, to make me ho - ly like you, to make me ho - ly like you.

ONE HOLY PASSION

Words by GEORGE BUTRON
Music by ANDY PARK

Bm7 G A
Ho - ly, ho - ly, ho - ly Lord God Al - might - y I a -
Gmaj7 C♯m7 F♯7sus Bm7 G
dore. Your glo - ry now my eyes can see, you're the
A F♯m7 Bm7 A/B D.S. al Coda Bm7 A/B To Coda
King who reigns in Maj - es - ty.
Em7 Cmaj7
One ho - ly pa - ssion now I know,
D A
as to a ru - ined world I go
Bm7 F♯m7
to kin - dle fire, spread a flame that will re -
G Em7 A Coda Bm7
veal your ho - ly name.

ONLY THE BLOOD

Words and Music by
BRIAN DOERKSEN

G C2 G D C
On - ly the blood of Je - sus cov-ers all of my sin,
G C2 G C D
on - ly the life of Je - sus re - news me from with - in.
Em9 C Am9 C/D D
Your blood is e- nough, your mer - cy com- plete.
Em9 C F D/F♯ G
Your work of a- tone- ment, paid for my debts, mak-ing me ho -
D.S. al Fine
C2 G C2 D G
Fine
ly. On - ly the blood of Je - sus.

OUR PRAYER

Words and Music by
CRAIG MUSSEAU

G/B C D
Em C/E D/F♯
Lord come and make us pure that we would be
G C D Em C/E
found with-out spot or stain. We will be read-y to meet
D/F♯ G C/G D D/C
you, we will dress our-selves in the fin - est lin - en. The
G/B C D2 D
righ - teous acts of the ones who love you.
C G D Em C G D Em D
Hear us, oh Lord. Breathe life in your church.

C G D Em C G

Come dwell with us. You are our God,

2nd time - D.S. al Coda

D Em D C *To Coda* G D Em C

we are your peop - le.

G D Em C G G2

Em C D/F♯

Lord come and make us one so that the

G C D

world will know the Fa - ther's love as

Em C D/F♯

Je - sus and the Fa - ther are one may we u -

G C D
nite — in — the full - ness — of Christ.

Em C/E D/F# G C/G
Lord our de-sire — is to know — you, and we want — to stay — close — to you..

D Em C/E D/F#
Let us fol - low you wher - ev - er you go, — don't let — us

G C/G D D/C G/B C
stray — from the Spir - it's call. — Let us — be known — as the friend

D
of God. —

Coda - Solo section

G D Em C G D Em C G D Em D C2

122

PHILIPPIANS II

Words and Music by
ANDY PARK

G A Bm
e - ven to death on a cross.
Em F♯m Bm
There-fore God ex - al-ted him to the ve - ry high-est plac
Em7 A Bm
and he gave to him the Name a-bove all names that
A Bm A G A F♯m7
ev'-ry knee should bow, and ev'-ry tongue con - fess
Bm Em A Bm
Je-sus Christ is Lord, he a-lone is Lord.
A Bm A G A F♯m7
Ev'-ry knee should bow, and ev'-ry tongue con - fess
Bm Em A F♯m7 Bm
Last time - D.C. al fine
Je-sus Christ is Lord, to the glo-ry of the Fa - ther.

PRAISE OUR GOD

(Psalm 66:8-20)

Words and Music by
ANDY PARK

D
Bm7
fall. He has pre - served our lives from the
free. You have pre - pared my heart and re -
C
G
D
C
en - e - my and he has not let — us — fall.
stored my mind, you have set my spir - it — free.
G
C2/G
1.
G
C2/G
2.
G
C2/G
I will
A
D2/A
A
D2/A
N.C.
(voices only)
Come and lis - ten you people, I will
tell you what he has done Come and lis - ten you peop - le, I will

D2
tell you what he has done He has done
E C♯m7 F♯m7 D A
might - y deeds of de - liv - er - ance, he has set the cap - tives
E C♯m7 D
free. He has done might - y deeds of de - liv - er - ance, he has
A
3
1. 2.
E
3.
E D
set the cap tives free. He has done free. He has set us free!
A D2/A A D2/A A D2/A D A

Praise our God, O peoples,

Let the sound of his praise be heard;

He has preserved our lives

and kept our feet from slipping.

Come and listen, all you who fear God;

Let me tell you what he has done for me.

I cried out to him with my mouth;

His praise was on my tongue.

- Psalm 66:8-9,16-17

PSALM 27

Words and Music by
DANNY DANIELS

Bm
A
D
Bm
A
one thing I ask, one thing that I de-
G
Bm
A
Bm
E7
sire, that I may dwell in the house of the Lord
D
A
Asus
A
Women echo: All of my
All of my life,
G
D
G
life, all of my life,
all of my life, all of my
D
G
A
D
3rd time -
D.S. al fine
all of my life.
(all of my)
life.
fine

PSALM 62

Words and Music by
SHARON HOWARTH

Am
F
G
Am
en.
My sal-va-tion and hon - or de - pend
F
G
Am
on him who is read - y to de - fend.
He is a
(You are my)
B♭
E
Am
F
G
3nd time -To Coda
might - y rock, my re-fuge and strength, my Lord and my
Am
2nd time To Coda
(for EGT solo)
Fmaj7
God.
Am7
Fmaj7
Am
G/A
Am
So I will trust in you

G/A Fmaj7 G/F Fmaj7 G/F
Lord at all times, pour out my
Gsus G Em7 Am G/A
heart to you, give you my life.
Am G/A Am G/A Am G/A
You are a might - y Rock and my Sal - va -
Fmaj7 F/G Fmaj7 F/G Gsus G
tion, you are my for - tress I know
Em7 Am G/A Am
I will not be shak - en.
D.S. 𝄋 al Coda
Coda
Fmaj7 G/F Fmaj7 G

Am G/A Am G/A Dm7 *D.S.* 𝄋

Coda

Am F G Am

God. My sal-va-tion and hon - or de - pend

F G Am

on him who is read - y to de - fend. You are my

B♭ E Am F G

might - y rock, my re-fuge and strength, my Lord and my

Repeat and ad lib

Am Fmaj7

God.

Am Dm7 Em E

PSALM 100

Words and Music by
ANDY PARK
♩ = 140
E B/E A2/E E B/E
Shout to the Lord
A2/E E B/E
for joy, all the earth. Wor-ship the Lord
A2/E E B
with glad - ness and joy-ful songs. Know that the Lord
A E A E B
is good, it is he who has made us. En-ter his gates
C♯m7 B F♯m7 E/G♯ A
with thanks, come in-to his courts with praise, come in-to his courts with

Bsus B No Chord E A/E E B A Esus
praise. For the Lord is good, and his love en-dures for ev-

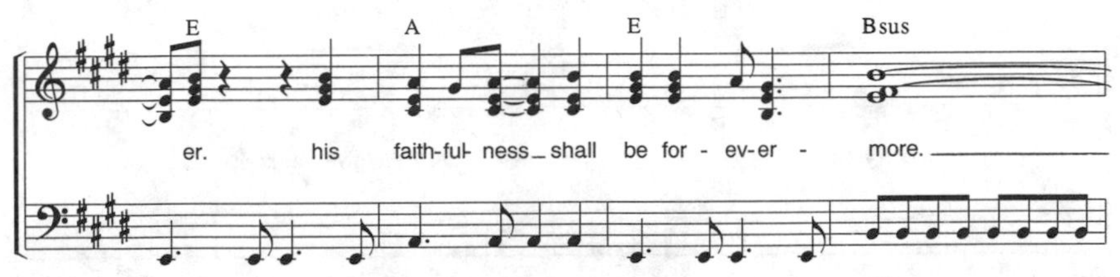
E A E Bsus
er. his faith-ful- ness shall be for - ev-er - more.

B E A/E E B A Esus
For the Lord is good, and his love en- dures for- ev-

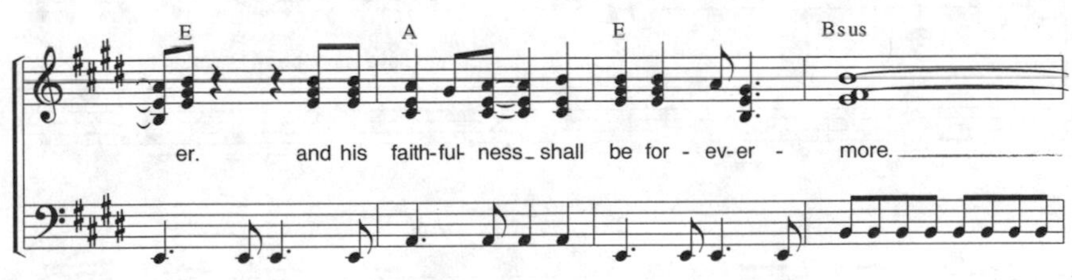
E A E Bsus
er. and his faith-ful- ness shall be for - ev-er - more.

N.C.
B E B/E A2/E E
For the Lord is good

PSALM 102

Words and Music by
KEVIN PROSCH

C
Dsus
D
G2
Gmaj9
vor, and the na-tions will fear___ your name, oh Lord. And we call out your name,_
Cmaj7/G
Gmaj7
C
Em
Am7
Dsus
D
you ne-ver change,_ you have no sha - dow of turn-ing at all.___ And we
To Coda
G2
Gmaj9
Cmaj7/G
Gmaj7
C
Em
lift up our cry_ in-to the night,_____ and ask for the cap - tives to be
D.C. al Coda
(take repeat)
CODA
2nd time - To Coda
Am
Dsus
D
Am7
Dsus
D
loosed from their chains._______
loosed from their chains._______
D.S. al Coda
G2
Gmaj9
Em
Em/D
C
Em
Am7
Dsus4
(ad lib lyrics)
Coda
G
Additional Lyrics
Verse 2: You looked down from heaven,
Your sanctuary high,
Heard the groans of the prisoners,
And those condemned to die.

RESTING PLACE
(Isaiah 66:1)
♩=91
Words and Music by
DAPHNE RADEMAKER
D G D
D G D
Heav - en is - my - throne — and earth is my foot - stool. —
G Asus
Where is — the - house - you will build for — me? —
A D G D
Whom of you - will - hear — the cry - of my — heart?

G
Asus
Where will my rest - ing place be?
A
Bm
G
D
Here oh Lord, have I pre- pared for you a home,
Asus
Bm
G
D
long have I de-sired for you to dwell.
Em
A/C#
Bm
G
D
Here oh Lord, have I pre pared a rest- ing place,
Asus
A
Em7
Asus
A
(D)
hear oh Lord, I wait for you a - lone.

SACRIFICE OF LOVE

Words and Music by
JOHN BARNETT

1.
2.
D/A A D G/A
D/A A Bm11
neath its crim-son flood. The ran-som for my sin. And
F♯m7 G F♯m7 Bm7
I'm for-ev-er grate-ful, and I will al ways.
Em7 A D Am7 G Em7
trust the pre - cious blood of Je-sus, the
To Coda
D.S. al Coda
D/A A Bm11 Bm/A G G6/A D Gmaj7 A/C♯
sac-ri-fice of love, the sac-ri-fice of love. The
Coda
Gmaj7/B A/C♯ G G6/A D
love.

SAVE US OH GOD
(Isaiah 56:7)
Words and Music by
KEVIN PROSCH
♩=88
G C G C
G C Am7 Dsus D
G/B C(add9) C G
We con -
C G C
fess the sins of our na-tion,
G C Am7
and Lord we are guil-ty of a prayer - less life.
D G C
We've turned a - way

G
C
G
our hearts from your laws,
and have tak-en for
C
Am7
Dsus
D
gran-ted
your un-chan - ging grace.
G
C
G
Turn a - way
this curse from our
C
G
C
coun-try.
We say that we've robbed you
and our
Am7
D
G
C
store hous-es are bare.
Op - en wide
G
C
G
the flood-gates of heaven.
Re-buke the de -

C
Am7
Dsus
G/B
vour-er so we may not be de-stroyed.
C
G
C
You said that if we'd hum-ble our-selves and be-gin to pray,
G
C
G
you would heal our bar - ren land, and
Am7
D
C
cleanse us with your rain. Don't pass us
G
C
G
by, let this be the gen-er-a-tion Lord,
C
G
D
that lifts up your name to all the world.

C
G
C
Save us oh God,
save a peop-le for your-
G
C
G
self, oh Lord.
Let the fear of the Lord
be their stan-
D
G
Am7
G/B
C
G
dard.
Save us oh God,
C
G
cleanse us from our un-faith-ful-ness.
Let the place where we
G
D
C
live be called a house
of prayer.
1. 2.
(2nd Time -
D.S. 𝄋 for guitar solo)
Last time
C
G/B
Am
G

SELAH

Music by
DAPHNE RADEMAKER

"Hear o Lord and answer me

For I am poor and needy

Guard my life for I am devoted to you

You are my God

Save your servant who trusts in you

Have mercy on me, o Lord

For I call to you all day long

Bring joy to your servant

For to you, o Lord

I lift up my soul"

-Psalm 86:1-4

148
SHOUT TO THE LORD
(Joshua 6:20)
Words and Music by
KEVIN PROSCH
We are his peop - le, he gives us mus- ic to sing.
There is a sound now, like the sound of the Lord when his en- e- mies flee.
But there is a cry

G Dsus D
in our hearts like when deep calls un - to the deep,
G C G D7sus
for your breath of de - liv - 'rance to breathe on the mus - ic we so
G D7sus Am7 Dsus D
des-p'rate - ly need. But with - out your pow - er
Am7 Dsus D Am7
3
all we have are these simp - le songs. If you'd step down from
Dsus D G/D D C/D D
heav - en, then the gates of hell would sure - ly fall.
G C
(So we) Shout to the Lord, shout to the Lord,

G D7sus D G C
shout to the Lord of hosts Shout to the Lord, shout
G D G D
to the Lord, shout to the Lord of hosts. And it
G C
breaks the heav-y yoke, breaks the heav-y yoke when you
G D7sus D G C
shout, you shout to the Lord. It breaks the heav-y yoke, breaks
G D G 1. D
the heav-y yoke when you shout, you shout to the Lord.
2. D7sus G D7sus G D7sus
Woa, you shout to the Lord, yea,

G
D7sus
G
D7sus
you shout to the Lord,
woa,
G
D7sus
G
D7sus
G
you shout to the Lord.
D7sus
G
D7sus
G
D7sus
G
G2sus
G
G2sus
G
G2sus
G
G2sus
La la la la la la la.
La la la la la la.
G
G2sus
G
G2sus
G
G2sus
G
G2sus
La la la la la la la.
La la la la la la.
Acoustic guitar and hi hat - keep rhythm going
G
C/G
G
Am/G
G
So we say: "Yes Lord, yes Lord."
Fine

SOFTEN MY HEART

Words and Music by
ANDY PARK

Em7
1. 3.
Asus
A
2. 4.
Asus
A
soft - en my heart to re - ceive.
soft - en the ground of my heart.
D
G
Asus
I want all that you have for me,
A
D
G
Asus
Je - sus, all that you have for me,
A
G
Asus
A
G
Op - en my un - der - stand - ing,
soft - en my heart to re - ceive.
Asus
A
D
G
A
D.C.
I want all that you have for
Last time only
D
A/D
A/G
D
me.
ritard

SONG FOR THE BRIDE

(Isaiah 30:15)

Words and Music by
BRIAN DOERKSEN

F♯m7 E B A
wait for me and hear my Spir - it say,
E Bsus E/G♯
"In re - pen-tance and rest is
A C♯m7 B E
your sal - va - tion. In qui - et - ness and
To Coda
Bsus E/G♯ A 1. E
trust is your strength,
3
2. E D.S. al Coda A/E E
strength, and
Coda
A C♯m7 B E/G♯ A E
your strength, is your strength.

156
SOVEREIGN LORD
(PSALM 71:14-18)
Words and Music by
CRAIG MUSSEAU
♩. = 56
1.3.
2.4.
Em A
But as for
Cmaj7 D G/B G
me, I will al - ways have hope.
Cmaj7 D C/G G
I will praise you more and more. My
Am7 D7sus G Em7 Am7
mouth will tell of your right - eous - ness. I will
D7sus G D/F♯ Em D D/C C
speak of your sal - va - tion though its

G C Am A/C♯ D D/F♯
full- ness_ is be-yond___ com - pare.___ I will come and pro-
G D D/F♯ G C C/B Am7 C/G
claim___ your might - y acts, O Sov-'reign Lord,___ Sov-'reign
D/F♯ C/E D D/F♯ G G/B D D/F♯
Lord.___ I will pro-claim___ your right - eous -
To Coda
D.S. al Coda
G C G/B Am7 C/G D
ness, yours_ a-lone,___ yours_ a-lone.___
Coda
D C D
(lone.)___

158 SPEAK NOW JESUS

Words and Music by
CRAIG MUSSEAU

G Bm7 C A/C♯ D A G
Je - sus, re-veal your heart to me. And I'll still my
D A G A/C♯ D C D/C
heart and set it a - part. For your word brings
C Bm7 Am7 D/A Am7 C/G
To Coda
peace to my wan - d'ring soul. I will wait
1. G
2. G D
D.S. al Coda
for you. for you. I'll
Coda
G D D7(no 3)/C D
for you.

160

TAKE OUR LIVES

(Romans 12:1-3)

Words and Music by
ANDY PARK

Em7
D
sac - ri - fice. Shine in us your
Em7 Am7 Bsus B Am7 C D
ho - ly light. Pu - ri - fy our
Em7 D C Bm7
hearts' de - sire, be to us a con -
Am7 Bm7 Em7 Cmaj7
sum - ing fire.
To Coda
Em7 Cmaj7
1.
2.
3x - ad lib
D.S.
Em7 Cmaj7 Em7 C/E D2/F♯
3.
D.S. al Coda
Coda
Em7 D2/F♯ Cmaj7 Em11
fire.

TENDER HEART

Words and Music by
TERRY BUTLER

E
C♯m7
Cmaj7
Bm7
love and com - pas - sion, your mer - cy and grace, be
E
C♯m7
Cmaj7
Bm7
known in my ac - tions, be seen on my face, in
Am7
B7sus
B7
all that I say or do, a ten - der heart.
Coda
Cmaj7
D6
2
2
Cmaj7
B/C♯
C♯
I need a ten - der heart. May your
F♯
D♯m7
Dmaj7
C♯m7
love and com - pas - sion, your me - rcy and grace, be
F♯
D♯m7
Dmaj7
C♯m7
known in my ac - tions, be seen on my face, in

2. Lord please give me a tender heart
One that is clothed in humility
Lord please give me a tender heart
Fill with your power and purity

I will give you a new heart

and put a new spirit in you;

I will remove from you

your heart of stone

and give you a heart of flesh.

- Ezekel 36:26

166

THE BLOOD OF JESUS

Words and Music by
MICHAEL J. PRITZL

D2 C2 D2
Heal me, cleanse me, cleanse me, with the
G D2 C2 G D2 Am7 C2
blood of Je - sus, wash- es white as snow. On the
To Coda
G D2 Am7 C Em9/B 1. D2
cross my Je - sus, you gave your life for
D.S. al Coda
Coda
Em9 2. D2 D2 C Em9/B
me. life. It's the life, yes you gave your
D2 C2 G2 C2
life for me. Pour the blood of Je-sus o - ver me.

168 THE LORD IS MY STRENGTH

Words and Music by
JOHN BARNETT

D E A E
he will not be moved. My rock, my for - tress, a

F♯m D A
might - y de - liv - er er, the glo - ry and lift - er of my

E
head, the song in my heart, the

F♯m D F♯m Bm F♯m E
joy of my sal - va - tion, the faith on which I stand,

A E/A D/A A D E A
he will not be_ moved.

THE LORD'S PRAYER

Words and Music by
BRIAN DOERKSEN & MICHAEL HANSEN

(repeat only on D.S.)
B♭/C F/C C2 B♭/C
Your king - dom come, your will be - done. Your king-dom come,
F/C C2 G F/A B♭2 F/A
your will be done, on the earth as it is in hea- ven.
C2 G G/B B♭2 F/A C2
Let it be done on the earth. A - men. A -
Fine
B♭2 F/A C2 G/F C/E G/F
men. Our Fath - er in hea - ven, ho- ly is your
D.S. al Fine
C/E G/F C/E G/F C2
name. For- give us our sins, Lord, as we for - give.

THERE'S NO ONE LIKE YOU

Words and Music by
EDDIE ESPINOSA

B
A6/E
E
I live just to seek your face. There's no one like
to serve you is my re - ward.
F♯m11
B
Esus
E
you my Lord, no one could take your place.
C♯m7
F♯m11
B
There's no one like you my Lord, no one like
E
E7
A
you. You are my God,
B/A
G♯m7
C♯m7
you're ev'-ry thing to me. There's no one like

F♯m7
B
E
you my Lord, no one like you.
E7
A
B/A
You are my God, you're ev'-ry thing to
G♯m7
C♯m7
F♯m7
me. There's no one like you my Lord,
B
Esus
1.
E
2.
E
no one like you. There's no one like
3.
E
F♯m11
E/G♯
A
A/B B
E

TRUST IN HIS LOVE

Words and Music by
JOHN WIMBER

1.
Em7
G/A
D
Gmaj7
G/A A
you can trust his love.
2.
Em7
G/A
You can trust his
Bm
love.
G
F♯m7
Em7
G/A
I tell you, you can trust his
D
love.
Gmaj9
F♯m7
Bm7
Gmaj7
F♯m7
Bm7
Em7
Gmaj9
F♯m7
Bm7
CODA:
Gmaj9
F♯m7
And I tell you,
Em7
D/F♯
G
F♯m7
Em7
G/A
D
you can trust, I tell you, you can trust his love.
ritard.

UNDIVIDED HEART

(Psalm 86:11)

Words and Music by
CINDY RETHMEIER
DAPHNE RADEMAKER
BRIAN DOERKSEN

178
D G D
vant. Give me an un - di - vid - ed heart
Am D G
that I may fear your name. Give me an un - div - id -
D C2 G/B
ed heart. No oth - er gods,
1. 3. Am
2nd Time D.S. al Coda
D
no oth - er love.
2. 4. Am D C2 G/B D
To Coda
No oth - er love. no oth - er gods, be - fore you.
Solo Section
D.S. after solo
C2 G/B Am7 D
Coda
C2 G/B Am D C2 G/B D
No oth - er gods, no oth - er love, no oth - er gods be fore you.
Fine

UNLIKE ANY OTHER

Words and Music by
RANDY, TERRY & GREG BUTLER

F
Gm7
E♭
F
Un - like an - y oth - er you rose from the grave.
Gm7
E♭
F
Un - like an - y oth - er you have pow - er to save. The
Gm7
E♭
F
tomb was found emp - ty, the stone rolled a - way. You're a - live,
A♭2
E♭/G
Cm7
F
You're a - live, you're a - live, you're a - live,
you're a-live, you're a-live.
1
E♭5/F
F5
G5/F
E♭5/F
Through your

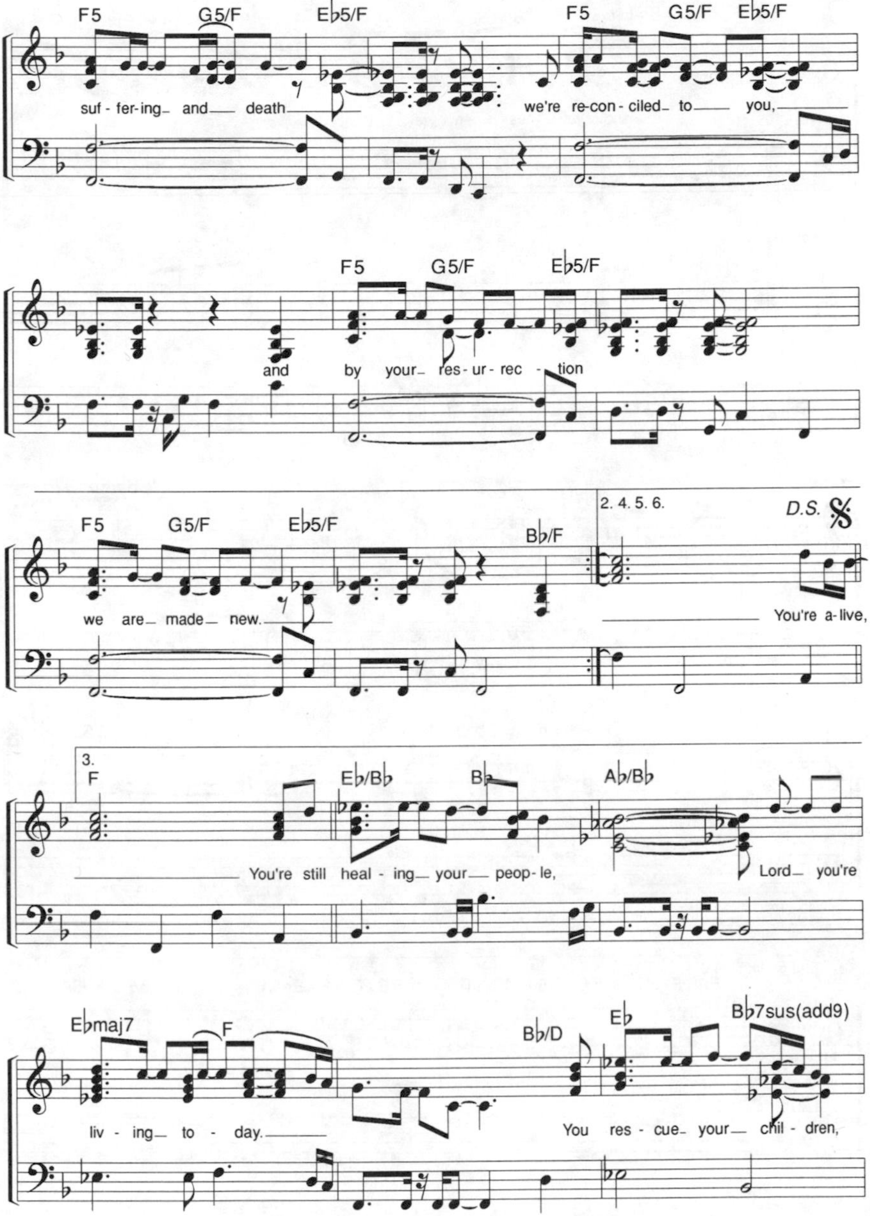
F5 G5/F E♭5/F F5 G5/F E♭5/F
suf - fer-ing and death we're re-con - ciled to you,
F5 G5/F E♭5/F
and by your res - ur - rec - tion
F5 G5/F E♭5/F B♭/F
we are made new.
2. 4. 5. 6.
D.S. 𝄋
You're a-live,
3.
F E♭/B♭ B♭ A♭/B♭
You're still heal - ing your peop - le, Lord you're
E♭maj7 F B♭/D E♭ B♭7sus(add9)
liv - ing to - day. You res - cue your chil - dren,

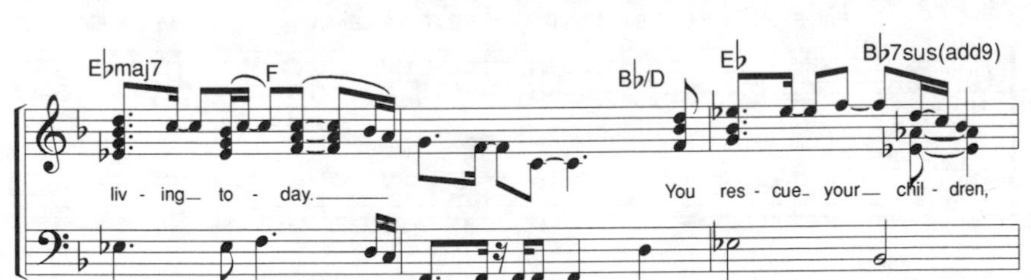

3. The tombs of all the others are filled with dead man's bones.
But you, oh Lord, are living and you're sitting on your throne.

WARRIOR KING

Words and Music by
HOLLAND DAVIS

F C G
we give you our ad - o - ra - tion,
we give you our ad - o - ra - tion,
for you are the wor - thy One,
for you are the ho - ly One,
F C G
we'll shout your name to ev' - ry na - tion.
we'll shout your name to ev' - ry na - tion.
Dm7 F C
Ho - ly are you Lord, might-y are your deeds.
G Dm7
Awe-some is your pow - er,

F
C
G
2.
Lord our war - rior King.
Ho ly are you Lord,
Dm7
F
C
G
might-y are your deeds.
Dm7
F
C
Awe-some is your pow - er,
Lord our war - rior King.
G
G
ad lib section
G
F
G

186

WE BEHOLD YOU

Words and Music by
DAVE SLANISKY

D
A
Lamb we be - hold.
Gmaj7
D
A
We be - hold you Lord.
Gmaj7
D
A
We stand in awe.
Bm7
D
A
We be - hold you.
Bm7
D
A
Last Time - D.C. al Fine
We be - hold you.

188

WE COME TO HUMBLE OURSELVES

Words and Music by
BRIAN DOERKSEN

1. 3.
2.
G
Dsus
D
D
ble our - selves.
selves.
G D/A G/B C G D
We come to hum - ble our -
D.C. al Coda
Coda
G C/G
Em D/F♯ C
selves.
throne of grace.
G Dsus G D D/F♯ G
We come to hum - ble our - selves.
C G D C
We come to hum - ble our - selves.

WE CRY OUT

Words and Music by
BEVERLY & TERRY BUTLER

2nd time -
Women echo: We cry out,
G
A
D
call on your name.
poor in your name.
We cry out,
we cry
we cry out, we cry out for this na - tion to
A
D
G
out,
we cry out for this na - tion to
come to the Lord.
We cry out,
D
A
D
come to the Lord.
We cry out,
we cry
we cry out, Lord we pray for sal - va - tion to
A
D/F♯
G
out,
Lord we pray for sal - va - tion to

F♯ Bm G D/A
come to this land. Lord we pray for your Spir - it to
G/A A 1. D 2. Gsus/C G/B G D A/C♯ A
fall on this land. land.
Gsus/C G/B G E B/D♯
We cry
Women echo: We cry out, we cry out, we cry
E B
out, we cry out, we cry
E A E B
out for this na - tion to come to the Lord. We cry

We cry out,
we cry out, Lord we
E
B
out, we cry out, Lord we
E/G♯
A
G♯
C♯m
pray for sal - va - tion to come to this land. Lord we
A
E/B
To Coda
D.S. al Coda
A/B
B
pray for your Spir - it to fall Lord we
Coda
Repeat - ad lib
A/B
B
E
G
A
fall on this land.
E
G
A
E

WE WILL EXALT YOU

Words and Music by
RANDY & TERRY BUTLER

D
Esus
Em7
D/F♯
Might - y God.
You are the child
G
D/G
D/E
born to us,
you are God's Son
giv'n to us,
Em7
Cmaj7
Am7
D
mer ci - ful Sav - ior of love,
Em - man - u - el,
1.
Cmaj7
D
Cmaj7
D
Em - man - u - el.
Em7
Em11
We will ex - alt
2.
Cmaj7
D
D/F♯
D.S.
You are the child
3.
Cmaj7
D
Cmaj7
D
Em11
(Em - man - u - el.)

WHATEVER IS TRUE

(Philippians 4:8,9)

Words and Music by
BRIAN DOERKSEN & CRAIG MUSSEAU

Gsus G C D G C D2 D2/C D2/B D2/A
love - ly. We will fix our thoughts on you.
G C G C G C G C G C G C G/D D G/D D
(Echo:) Je - sus, who is like you? Je - sus, who is like you?
Je - sus, who is like you? Je - sus, who is like you?
G C G C G C G C G C G C
Je - sus, who is like you? Je - sus,
Je - sus, who is like you? Je - sus, who is
To Coda
1. 2. 2nd Time - D.S. al Coda
G/D D G/D D C6 9
who is like you, who is like you?
like you? Who is like you?
Repeat as often as desired for spontaneous worship
Coda
D/C C D/C C G/D D G/D D D/C C D/C C C6 9
like you?

198
WHO IS LIKE YOU?
♩=135
Words adapted from Psalm 89:1-2, 5-8
Music by ANDY PARK
Am7 Fmaj7 Em7
Am7 Fmaj7 Em7
I will sing of the Lord's great love for - ev - er,
There is none in the heav-ens who is like you. The
Am7 Fmaj7 Em7
with my mouth will I make known his faith-ful-ness. I will de -
ho - ly ones in the heav-ens great - ly fear you. The heav-ens
Dm7 Em7 Am7
clare his love stands firm. I will de -
praise your faith- ful - ness. The heav-ens
Dm7 Em7 Am7 Am G Fmaj7 Em7
clare his love stands firm. O Lord God Al -
praise your faith-ful - ness.

F
Em7
Am
might - y, who is like you? You are
F
Em7
Am
G Fmaj7 Em7
might - y and your faith - ful-ness sur - rounds you. O Lord God Al -
F
Em7
Am
might - y, who is like you? You are
3rd Time - D.S. al Coda
4th Time - To Coda
F
Em7
Am G Am
might - y and your faith - ful ness sur - rounds you.
2.
4th time - D.S.
Dm7
Em7
Am7
Coda
Am
F
Em7
Am G
Am
You are might - y and your faith - ful-ness sur - rounds you.

200 WHO WOULD NOT LOVE YOU?

Words and Music by
JOHN BARNETT

C6 Am7 D2
serve you all their days? Who would not
G2 Em11 Em7
praise you, who would not hon - or you, who would not
C6 D2 G2 C2/G
1.
die for you, who would not love you? A
2.
G2 Em11 Em7
(ad lib lyrics)
C2 Am7 D2 G2

WORTHY IS THE LAMB

Words and Music by
CARL TUTTLE

"Holy, holy, holy

is the Lord God Almighty,

who was, and is, and is to

come."

-Revelation 4: 8

YOU ARE MY KING

Words and Music by
BRIAN DOERKSEN

F♯m7 D A/E E 1. D

you now. All of my life, I glad - ly give to you.

2. 3. D F♯m7 D

You are my you, plac-ing my hopes and dreams, in your hands, I

A/E E D A E Bm7 F♯m7

give my heart to you. I love you, love you,

𝄋𝄋 D E A E Bm7 F♯m7 D E

D.S.S. - 2 times

Je - sus. Yes I love you, love you, Je - sus my King.

A E/A F♯m11 *To Coda* 𝄌 A E/A F♯m11 *D.S.* 𝄋 *al Coda*

You are my

𝄌*Coda* *Repeat as needed for ad lib*

A E/A F♯m11 A

YOU WILL REIGN

Words and Music by
ANDY PARK

Asus
A
D
F
High.
You are the King of
G
D
F
all the earth,
you are the Lord of all
G
C G
D
F
na - tions;
You crush your en - e- mies
G
D2
B♭
un - der your feet,
Je - sus Christ, our
A7sus
A
D
1st time D.S.
Lord,
the King!
Fine

208

YOUR SERVANTS

(NEH. 1:10,11)

♩=89

Words and Music by
EDDIE ESPINOSA & CINDY RETHMEIER

C G

D C G
Here we are, your servants, your people
D C D Em7
whom you've redeemed by your great strength and mighty hand. O

G C C/D
are, we are your ser - vants. Here we
G C G/B
are, we are your peo - ple, and
Am7 D Dsus D G C/G 1. G 2. G D/F♯
you are our God. Here we
Em7 G/B C C/E D/F♯
are, we are your ser - vants. Here we
G C G/B
are, we are your peo - ple, and
Am7 D Dsus D G C/G G G/B
you are our God.
(Yes)
(And)
Fine

WORSHIP PRODUCT AVAILABLE FROM VINEYARD MUSIC GROUP

Continued...

KIDS

9106 Worship For Kids 1
Cassette Only

9111 Worship For Kids 2
Cassette Only

9125 Worship For Kids 3
Cassette Only

9136 Worship For Kids 4
Cassette Only

SPECIALTY ALBUMS

9129 A Vineyard Christmas

9160 Vineyard Celebration

9173 Resurrection Celebration

9174 Con Mis Labios - Spanish Worship

9182 Contemporary Hymns & Classic Choruses

9185 A Christmas Celebration

SONGBOOKS

FLB9100 Songs Of The Vineyard Volume 1

FLB9121 Songs Of The Vineyard Volume 2

FLB9145 Songs Of The Vineyard Volume 3

FLB9165 Songs Of The Vineyard Volume 4

VNB9170 Songs Of The Vineyard Volume 5